Ten Poems
about Libraries

Candlestick Press

Published by:
Candlestick Press,
Diversity House, 72 Nottingham Road, Arnold, Nottingham NG5 6LF
www.candlestickpress.co.uk

Design and typesetting by Craig Twigg

Printed by Bayliss Printing Company Ltd of Worksop, UK

Selection and Introduction © Lorraine Mariner, 2024

Cover illustration © Laura Brett, 2024
https://lawsdraws.com/

Candlestick Press monogram © Barbara Shaw, 2008

© Candlestick Press, 2024

ISBN 978 1 913627 34 8

Acknowledgements

The poems in this pamphlet are reprinted from the following books, all by
permission of the publishers listed unless stated otherwise. Every effort has been
made to trace the copyright holders of the poems published in this book. The
editor and publisher apologise if any material has been included without
permission, or without the appropriate acknowledgement, and would be glad to
be told of anyone who has not been consulted.

Thanks are due to all the copyright holders cited below for their kind permission.

Adrian Buckner, *See Saw* (Leafe Presse, 2023). Claire Crowther, *A Pair of Three*
(Shearsman Books, Bristol, 2022) by kind permission of the author. Rita Dove,
On the Bus with Rosa Parks (WW Norton & Co., 1999) Copyright © 1999 by
Rita Dove. Used by permission of WW Norton & Company, Inc. Martina Evans,
The Windows of Graceland: New and Selected Poems (Carcanet Press, 2016).
Edward Hirsh, *Special Orders* (Alfred A. Knopf, 2008) by kind permission of the
author. Lorraine Mariner, poem was specially commissioned for this pamphlet.
Ian McMillan, *Talking Myself Home* (John Murray Press) by kind permission of
Macmillan/Picador. Indigo Williams, the poem was a commission from the
National Poetry Library for their anniversary celebration, used here by kind
permission of the author.

All permissions cleared courtesy of Dr Suzanne Fairless-Aitken –
Swift Permissions swiftpermissions@gmail.com

Where poets are no longer living, their dates are given.

Introduction

I've worked as a librarian for over twenty-five years now, sixteen of those in the National Poetry Library at the Southbank Centre, London. One of the poems I've selected, 'Eugene' by Indigo Williams, was written to celebrate the National Poetry Library turning 60 and it's turning 70 as I write this. I'm part of a long tradition of poet-librarians, the most famous being Philip Larkin, and I was really excited to discover recently that poets Marianne Moore and Audre Lorde worked for a time as librarians too. I definitely feel there are similarities between librarianship and writing poems – putting things into order and focusing on the detail. The blank space around the words of a poem on the page could also be the quiet space of a library that librarians protect, though I've never actually put my finger to my lips and told anybody to *shush*.

But the poems I've chosen here are not written by librarians (as far as I know). I think maybe when you're working in a library, whatever noble reasons called you to that profession, it can become just another job that pays your bills with the stresses and strains work can bring. It's still the "toad *work*", which squats on Larkin's life in his poem 'Toads' and not the sacred space of many of these poems.

The selection captures the excitement of libraries for children, a place where they make discoveries watched over by benevolent librarians (possibly celestial beings according to Charles Simic). It also expresses the longing to return to that place of safety and freedom that adults experience. Books sing from the shelves and two of the poems refer to "greed" as the narrators devour the words that they need.

The poems remind me why libraries, especially public ones, are so important and should be protected. And they remind me why I chose to become a librarian and why I work in a library still.

Lorraine Mariner

The Mobile Library

It came once a fortnight
and I went under the beds,
scrabbling for overdue books,
balls of fluff as big as mice
skating across the linoleum.

It parked at the cross
for I don't know how long
and sometimes if I wasn't ready
with the books, I'd look out
and it would be gone.

Why didn't you warn me sooner?
I'd run out breathing anxious breaths
that tasted like frozen lemonade.

And that was the best thing,
when I was sure that it was still there,
my feet pressing into the deep steps.

Martina Evans

Maple Valley Branch Library, 1967

For a fifteen-year-old there was plenty
to do: Browse the magazines,
slip into the Adult Section to see
what vast *tristesse* was born of rush-hour traffic,
décolletés, and the plague of too much money.
There was so much to discover – how to
lay out a road, the language of flowers,
and the place of women in the tribe of Moost.
There were equations elegant as a French twist,
fractal geometry's unwinding maple leaf;

I could follow, step-by-step, the slow disclosure
of a pineapple Jell-O mold – or take
the path of Harold's purple crayon through
the bedroom window and onto a lavender
spill of stars. Oh, I could walk any aisle
and smell wisdom, put a hand out to touch
the rough curve of bound leather,
the harsh parchment of dreams.

As for the improbable librarian
with her salt and paprika upsweep,
her British accent and sweater clip
(mom of a kid I knew from school) –
I'd go up to her desk and ask for help
on bareback rodeo or binary codes,
phonics, Gestalt theory,
lead poisoning in the Late Roman Empire,
the play of light in Dutch Renaissance painting;
I would claim to be researching
pre-Columbian pottery or Chinese foot-binding,
but all I wanted to know was:
Tell me what you've read that keeps
that half smile afloat
above the collar of your impeccable blouse.

So I read *Gone with the Wind* because
it was big, and haiku because they were small.
I studied history for its rhapsody of dates,
lingered over Cubist art for the way
it showed all sides of a guitar at once.
All the time in the world was there, and sometimes
all the world on a single page.
As much as I could hold
on my plastic card's imprint I took,

greedily: six books, six volumes of bliss,
the stuff we humans are made of:
words and sighs and silence,
ink and whips, Brahma and cosine,
corsets and poetry and blood sugar levels –
I carried it home, past five blocks of aluminum siding
and the old garage where, on its boarded-up doors,
someone had scrawled:

I CAN EAT AN ELEPHANT
IF I TAKE SMALL BITES.

Yes, I said, to no one in particular: *That's*
what I'm gonna do!

Rita Dove

Branch Library

I wish I could find that skinny, long-beaked boy
who perched in the branches of the old branch library.

He spent the Sabbath flying between the wobbly stacks
and the flimsy wooden tables on the second floor,

pecking at nuts, nesting in broken spines, scratching
notes under his own corner patch of sky.

I'd give anything to find that birdy boy again
bursting out into the dusky blue afternoon

with his satchel of scrawls and scribbles,
radiating heat, singing with joy.

Edward Hirsch

The Librarian at Her Post

Sometimes I am a lifeguard
at a swimming pool in need of a whistle –
no shouting, no petting, no bombing
though I'm not sure who I'm rescuing
sneaking up on people to check
they're not just here for free Wi-Fi.

And sometimes I am a sentry
defending the castle against marauders,
those who think everything is for sale,
those that believe in censorship, spurred on
by the librarians of America holding fast
against the banning of another book.

And sometimes I am an usher
at a wedding, when a person enters as if
they're stepping into a cathedral, the one
the duchess filled with trees. My armour
melts away and I say *Yes, this place really exists,
I've been keeping it safe for you.*

Lorraine Mariner

Lady of The Issuing Desk

Wednesday afternoon, three forty-five: I sit
browsing the newspapers in the soft seats

of one of the County Library's smaller outlets.
But for a particular chain of events involving

a changed plan and a lost key I might never again
have been out of the rush, out of the way of things

in quite the same way as one is out of the rush,
out of the way of things, browsing the newspapers

in the soft seats of one of the County Library's smaller
outlets at three forty-five on a Wednesday afternoon.

Oh Lady of the issuing desk, how saintly you appear –
your only currency is helpfulness, serial acts of

kindness and no-trouble-at-all-dear. Filling an enquiry
free moment (there are many) you tidy the stack

of children's toys, stained and grubby like so many
good intentions, then swish back to your station,

the benevolent and ordered face of a quiet world.
I close my eyes, absorb your footfall and the noise

in the air from your long skirt. In this world I never
rebelled, never gave my ticket to another child

nor returned a book late with a dog-eared excuse.
Oh Lady of the issuing desk, I long for your smile,

for I live in the rush, in the way of things,
out there in the wintry twilight.

Adrian Buckner

In A Library

THE living ofttimes vex us –
The wise old dead are best –
When Life's vain games perplex us
'T is here we turn for rest.

Louise Chandler Moulton (1835 – 1908)

Eugene

Tonight, I am busy with words the day forgot to say, like 'Hello',
to the man who reads every Sunday outside the Poetry Library
whose beard and afro weeds into a bushy maze.
He doesn't remember me, but 8 years ago we were both stock
assistants stacking rails with clothes we couldn't afford.
I heard he lost the tender in his eyes to a small fire that started in his brain
but thawed his left side till he was half smoke half frame.
He carries everything he knows in a black bin bag
and reads out loud to remember. Today I saw him
pile books on the table like a feast, while I, greedy poet,
didn't stop to share a word.

Indigo Williams

Helicity from the Library Basement

The stair began where I sat
        and circled to the top. Then nipped the flank
of blue sky through a lantern.

It began at my chair when
        I turned the three hundredth or so page. That
was the second I saw. Soared

up two floors. Swooshing steps flashed
        into someone else's trajectory
of unknowingness. Just bulk

of back bearing a book bag
        as usual. One by one they climbed past
the other rockface readers.

I saw sun through the risers.
        Big universe whose self I took. Small bang
in my head was hers. I gave

as would a white-footed mouse
        share ticks with any human: ticks and selves
testimonies to hostage

or vectors swirling disease.
        I'm back by the stacks. Still the long straight shelves
stand. Arc over arc of oak

banisters run floor to roof.
        Books, stop staring. I've told you. And you, words,
whirl. You're a choir. You'll be heard.

Claire Crowther

In the Library
for Octavio

There's a book called
'A Dictionary of Angels.'
No one has opened it in fifty years,
I know, because when I did,
The covers creaked, the pages
Crumbled. There I discovered

The angels were once as plentiful
As species of flies.
The sky at dusk
Used to be thick with them.
You had to wave both arms
Just to keep them away.

Now the sun is shining
Through the tall windows.
The library is a quiet place.
Angels and gods huddled
In dark unopened books.
The great secret lies
On some shelf Miss Jones
Passes every day on her rounds.

She's very tall, so she keeps
Her head tipped as if listening.
The books are whispering.
I hear nothing, but she does.

Charles Simic (1938 – 2023)

Adult Fiction

I always loved libraries, the quiet of them,
The smell of the plastic covers and the paper
And the tables and the silence of them,
The silence of them that if you listened wasn't silence,
It was the murmur of stories held for years on shelves
And the soft clicking of the date stamp,
The soft clickety-clicking of the date stamp.

I used to go down to our little library on a Friday night
In late summer, just as autumn was thinking about
Turning up, and the light outside would be the colour
Of an Everyman cover and the lights in the library
Would be soft as anything, and I'd sit at a table
And flick through a book and fall in love
With the turning of the leaves, the turning of the leaves.

And then at seven o'clock Mrs Dove would say
In a voice that wasn't too loud so it wouldn't
Disturb the books 'Seven o'clock please ...'
And as I was the only one in the library's late summer rooms
I would be the only one to stand up and close my book
And put it back on the shelf with a sound like a kiss,
Back on the shelf with a sound like a kiss.

And I'd go out of the library and Mrs Dove would stand
For a moment silhouetted by the Adult Fiction,
And then she would turn the light off and lock the door
And go to her little car and drive off into the night
That was slowly turning the colour of ink and I would stand
For two minutes and then I'd walk over to the dark library
And just stand in front of the dark library.

Ian McMillan

The Repair and Maintenance of Glass in Churches

by
Jill Kerr

CHURCH HOUSE PUBLISHING
Great Smith Street, London SW1P 3NZ

ISBN 0 7151 7560 2

Published 1991 for the Council for the Care of Churches by Church House Publishing.

Printed in England by TAS PRINT LTD.

CONTENTS

INTRODUCTION

This booklet is adapted from my chapter on the Repair and Maintenance of Historic Glass published in *Practical Building Conservation*, English Heritage Technical Handbook, Volume 5, (see Bibliography).

It is written to help those who are faced with responsibility for stained and painted window glass – and for those fortunate enough to have that rare survival, historic plain glazing. The subjects covered are devised to deal with most of the difficulties we at English Heritage are asked about most frequently. Like all important issues, much of what I have written is basic commonsense requiring no specialist knowledge. In recognition that it will be read by non-specialists, I have attempted to explain and describe in a straightforward and direct style. This has inevitably lead to simplification of complex issues and no doubt the omission of certain aspects of particular interest to you. I would therefore like to enlist your assistance in drawing my attention to lapses, lacunae and lack of clarity so that any future edition can be amended accordingly.

For the writing of this booklet, my original text has benefited from the critical attention of my colleagues of the International Corpus Vitrearum Technical Forum. I would especially like to acknowledge the help of Dr Ernst Bacher of the Institut für Österreichische Kunstforschung des Bundesdenkmalamtes, Vienna, Dr Jean-Marie Bettembourg of the Laboratoire de Recherche des Monuments Historiques, France, Dr Yvette Vanden Bemden of Belgium, Dr Stephan Trumpler of Switzerland and Drs Janse and Crevecoeur of Holland. I am also grateful for the professional and technical advice of Ian Curry, Harry Fairhurst, David O'Connor, Roy Newton, Keith Barley, Alan Younger and Alfred Fisher, and the specialist knowledge of Dr Barry Knight of English Heritage's Ancient Monuments Laboratory who has kindly permitted me to reproduce his lead came typology. Anthony Rossi has also generously allowed the reproduction of his exemplary and lucid specification drawings. I would also like to express my thanks to Jonathan Goodchild for his editorial assistance and courteous comments on my text.

WHAT GLASS IS

Glass is a complex man-made, non-crystalline material. The basic ingredient, natural silica in the form of fine sand or flint, was fused with alkaline fluxes such as soda and potash and other ingredients including lime and cullet (broken glass). After the molten glass was formed into the required shape, it was annealed and cooled slowly and evenly to strengthen its infrastructure by removing the stresses that had built up during manufacture; it was then ready to be cut.

The technology for glass making existed in Europe 4,000-5,000 years ago. Window glass was introduced into Britain by the Romans. The history of glass manufacture is extensive and, as it is not possible to summarise it simply, it is not included in this booklet. Further information on window glass technology and manufacture can be obtained from the references listed on page 55.

Glass is a very vulnerable and brittle medium which decays due to factors which are inherent in it, external to it, or a combination of both. A useful list for further reading into the complex mechanisms of glass corrosion and well-illustrated histories of how stained and painted window glass is designed and made is also given in the Bibliography.

PROFESSIONAL ADVICE AND CRAFT SKILLS

Those who work on or make decisions regarding historic window glass must understand the complicated nature of the material itself: the way it is fitted into the window, how it relates to the building and its historic context. It is also necessary to be aware of the way the window is interacting with its environment, its relationship to the ventilation of the building and the combined effect of all these related factors. A professional conservation glazier's report should address all these issues and analyse the causes of any problems before proposing any solutions.

Glazing should never be considered in isolation from its structural context. All work on glass involves work to related fixtures and fittings be they brick, stone, mastic, mortar, wood, iron, render, plaster or paint. It is always essential therefore that you involve your architect, who will not only have knowledge of the associated physical problems, but may well also be able to advise you of suitable glaziers to tender for the work on the basis of his specification. Your architect will know whether to recommend you to a general practitioner or a specialist for the work required. For further advice on specialist conservators see page 53.

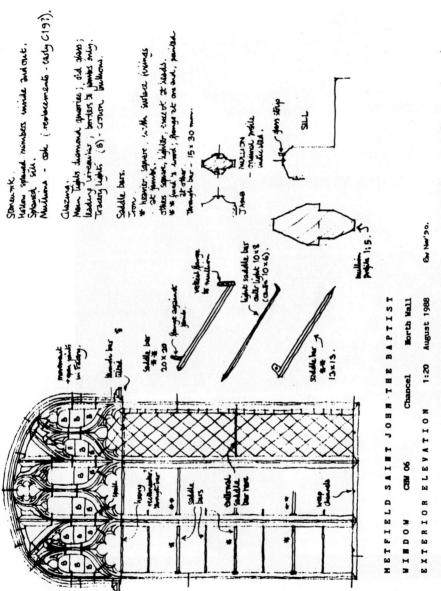

METFIELD SAINT JOHN THE BAPTIST

WINDOW   **CBW 06**   Chancel   North Wall

EXTERIOR ELEVATION   1:20   August 1988   By Nov'90.

An excellent analytical drawing of an entire window, its structure and materials before repair work. Reproduced by kind permission of Anthony Rossi.

3

Before cleaning. Kirk Sandall (Yorks).
Photo: Keith Barley.

4

Conservation cleaning by a specialist. Surface dirt has been removed and the legibility of the figure improved by careful completion of the missing hand and arm of the cross. The new pieces are signed and dated and the principles of reversibility and recording scrupulously observed. The original glass retains its patina, corrosion and character after cleaning. Kirk Sandall (Yorks).
Photo: Keith Barley.

CONSERVATION PRINCIPLES

There are three basic principles applicable to the conservation of all types of historic glass. These should be borne in mind whenever work is proposed or undertaken.

'Conservation' of historic glass means that every attempt is made to keep as much of the original glass, lead, ferramenta and surrounding masonry as possible.

Minimum intervention

Current practices of glass conservation are based on the principle of doing as little as possible to the glass. Some glass can be cleaned *in situ,* some without stripping the leads. It is extremely important that the expectation of dramatic transformations of the glass is not fostered. Ancient glass will never clean up bright and shiny as new. If that is what you have in mind, why not commission some contemporary glass yourself which will live up to your expectations? Most conservators will advocate the removal of harmful and damaging dirt and corrosion products, the increase of legibility by the removal of lead lines disturbing designs, and perhaps the replacement of missing features using backingplates (see below p.36). The rearrangement of ancient glass and the removal of subsequent additions and repairs is not usually encouraged, as the arrangement of the glass before conservation may be part of its history and intrinsically worthy of preservation. Speculative and gratuitous rearrangements have destroyed a significant amount of historical evidence and must be avoided. The 'leave as found' principle is the primary concern of current conservation practice. Any departure from this basic principle must be fully argued, justified and recorded.

Full recording

A full record should be made of your glass by the conservator before work commences. Photographs should be taken and details of particular problems will be recorded on the lead rubbings before and during conservation as work progresses. The CVMA/Council for the Care of Churches method of recording is now an accepted part of all grant-aided glass conservation, and the cost of it is built-in to the conservator's estimate. (Full details are available from English

Heritage or the Council for the Care of Churches and are published in *Practical Building Conservation* Volume 5.) This documentation will be invaluable to your successors as well as a responsible protection of your investment today. Inadequate records of previous restorations are a major problem for today's conservators, and valuable time and resources have been diverted to researching this past work.

The importance of keeping full dated photographic records of glass – even if no conservation work is envisaged – cannot be emphasised strongly enough. Glass is always at risk from some threat or other and requires the safeguard of proper recording even if no actual work is to be undertaken. In the event of vandalism or breakage this record will help your insurance assessors and the craftsman who will have the job of reconstruction. Copies of records can be sent to the CVMA Archive at the National Monuments Record where advice can be sought on all aspects of recording glass *in situ*. They will also advise on auxiliary material such as original designs, cartoons or drawings the artist may have given the church. (See p.53 'Sources of Information' for details.)

Reversibility of techniques

It is a paramount principle that all techniques used in glass conservation must be reversible. This eliminates many of the damaging methods used in the past such as the application of chemical coatings, the refiring and repainting of historic glass and the destruction of historically important arrangements. No reversible techniques have so far been developed for the fixing of loose paint.

Exchange of professional experiences – foreign glass

These three principles of full recording, minimum intervention, and reversibility of techniques are the basic rules to follow for the cleaning and repair of all types of glass. The sharing of experience and knowledge, success and failure should be part of all professional conservation. It is rare to encounter a problem in conserving glass which has not been experienced by another specialist from whom much could be learned. This is particularly important when dealing with foreign glass, where communication with the experts in the country of origin is essential in keeping up-to-date with evolving techniques and methods. If you have a particular problem with glass of foreign origin – and there is a surprising amount in our parish churches – it is advisable to seek advice from the Council for the Care of Churches who will be able to refer you and your architect to a specialist who has experience in dealing with your type of glass.

THE INSPECTION AND CONSERVATION OF LEAD CAMES

Lead cames hold the glass pieces together in such a way that the window is flexible and able to respond to the expansion and contraction caused by daily and seasonal temperature changes, as well as temperature differential between the inside and the outside of the building. Most important, leads are also historical documents and should be considered an integral part of the design.

In the Middle Ages, the glass designer minimised the inconvenience of having to change the glass every time he needed to change the colour by carefully integrating the cames into the design. It is often forgotten that we are frequently looking at medieval glass through a disfiguring network of supervening mending leads inserted by subsequent repairers, restorers and jobbing plumbers. This point was often misunderstood by the glass designers during the Gothic Revival who frequently produced glass without integrated lead lines, following their own design rather than the logic of the deployment of colour and line the medieval glazier would have used. It is actually possible for an experienced conservator of glass to restore the legibility of incoherent medieval glass by reconstructing the original cut lines. It is also possible in some cases for a glass historian to recover lost iconography by studying the surviving lead pattern.

A rubbing of the lead pattern must be made by your conservator before the glass is dismantled. This will serve as the basis for the actual record of the restoration and provide the working cartoon for the reconstruction of the panel and the laying out for reglazing. It is important that the leads are examined in detail for evidence of the extent and date of previous repairs and releading and, in some cases, inscriptions of signatures and dates. As all lead cames eventually relax and deteriorate due to their continual movement, all glass requires releading at intervals in its life. Because of this, the survival of medieval cames is very rare, which makes their recognition, recording and retention where possible even more important. Present principles of conservation favour the retention of medieval leads wherever

MEDIEVAL WINDOW LEAD PROFILES

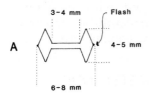

A

Type A has thick diamond-shaped flanges and a prominent casting flash along the outside edge. It was cast in a hinged two-piece mould about 50cm long.

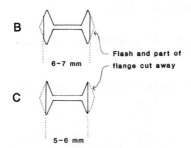

B

C

Types B and C have been made from cast came as type A by scraping off the casting flash. The only difference between them is in the amount of lead removed from the flange.

There is considerable variation in types A, B and C, even in the same piece, because each length is made by hand.

POST-MEDIEVAL WINDOW LEAD PROFILES

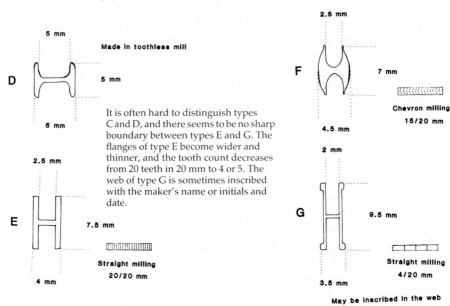

It is often hard to distinguish types C and D, and there seems to be no sharp boundary between types E and G. The flanges of type E become wider and thinner, and the tooth count decreases from 20 teeth in 20 mm to 4 or 5. The web of type G is sometimes inscribed with the maker's name or initials and date.

A chronology of the profiles and methods of manufacture of lead cames in medieval and post-medieval windows.
Reproduced by kind permission of Dr Barry Knight.

9

possible, the glass they hold being cleaned in the leads and any strengthening necessary being carried out with sympathy and restraint. At the present rate of releading, sixteenth-, seventeenth- and eighteenth-century cames will soon become equally rare.

FERRAMENTA AND FIXING METHODS

Various methods have been used for fixing glass into window openings. Some of these are of particular historic importance and should never be removed or destroyed as they can provide essential evidence for the reconstruction of lost glazing programmes or information on technological developments.

This is particularly so in the case of medieval ferramenta where the survival of the armatures, the iron infrastructure constructed in geometrically symmetrical patterns to whose frames the panels of original glass were pegged in place, can survive intact, glazed with nineteenth-century reticulated white quarries. While this is a ghost of the medieval glazing programme, it can be indicative of the actual number of scenes selected from, for example, the life of the saint whose altar was once located beneath the window. Such survivals generally occur in cathedrals such as Canterbury or Ely, but equally interesting evidence for early examples of window fitments can be clearly observed in the frames of many buildings sacred and secular. Hinges for shutters, rebates for the insertion of wooden frames which contained horn or oiled cloth, chamfered glazing grooves and holes in the window frames for pegs can all be of interest to glass historians. Nothing should be destroyed or removed without knowing what it is or at least recording it.

Non-ferrous tips can always be added to ancient tie bars or metal grilles, so that rust disruption of the masonry into which they are fixed is prevented. The techniques of preserving and extending the protection of the surface and the life of corroded iron are well established. Your architect should refer to what regular maintenance should be undertaken in his Quinquennial Inspection Report. (*Practical Building Conservation* Volume 4, Chapter 2 gives full details. Bibliography p.55.) See also *A Guide to Church Inspection and Repair* (Bibliography p.55) on the workings of the quinquennial inspection system. A blacksmith working with a specialist conservation glazier can retain, restore or copy decorative features such as casement hinges and handles.

Disfiguring fixing with mismatched mortar. This window has been refixed into the stonework without an architect's involvement. The result is a glaring aesthetic disaster which has already begun to fail with cracks and fissures because the 'mix' is too hard for the soft sandstone surround. Streaks are just visible on the surface of the single sheet of glass cemented over the medieval glass. The external sheet is unventilated and rigidly fixed. Photo: J Kerr.

11

An important detail, often overlooked, is the composition of the mortar bedding with which the glass is glazed into the groove of the masonry frame or into which the ferramenta are fixed. If the mortar is too hard, badly placed so that it spills over onto the glass beyond the lead edge flange, the wrong colour for the adjacent stonework or inexpertly applied, it can not only disfigure the appearance of the church seriously, it can also be a source of damage to both glass and fabric. Dense cementitious mortar fixings also create difficulties for future deglazing – which will certainly be necessary at some time. The removal of all such mortars may require the use of potentially damaging techniques such as mechanical drills or grinders. If fixing glass is undertaken in an inexperienced way, both the fabric of your church and the glass may be damaged beyond repair. This is particularly problematic when there is no sacrificial fillet framing the outer edge of each glass panel. Your architect should always instruct the glazier by specifying the constituents, proportions, colour and technique of the mortar manufacture and identifying any physical problems relating either to the fabric or the architectural context into which the glass is to be set. If necessary a mason or a blacksmith can be brought in under architectural supervision to work with the glazier.

THE DIAGNOSIS AND TREATMENT OF GLAZING DEFECTS

Glass is a vulnerable and brittle medium which should be inspected frequently to ensure that any changes, however undramatic, are observed and recorded. Even small changes should be notified to your architect with sufficient clarity for him to decide whether a more detailed inspection is necessary.

Historical glass can be adversely affected by many factors external to it. It can at times even become linked into the transfer of the loads of a structure to the ground. As the weakest link, it will be the first to exhibit signs of distress, indicating that rectification of a structural problem is necesssary.

The following defects are the most commonly experienced in window glazing. The causes of these and appropriate remedial actions are discussed.

Undulating or buckling panels

The principal causes of undulating or buckling panels are failure of the leading, inadequate tying or support, oversized panels, too much movement, the panel being too rigidly glazed or fixed without adequate allowance for expansion or contraction, and slippage of the support system. The presence of too many horizontal leads in a window can result in structural failure as leads in this orientation are vulnerable to overloading. A classic example of this is associated with poorly designed and glazed plain glazing based on horizontal and vertical grid patterns. The leads at the base give way under cumulative weight they have to bear from the panels above and, because the weight is not transmitted evenly across the whole surface, this creates characteristic zig-zag deformation. This type of failure rarely occurs with the diagonal leading pattern of diamond quarry glazing, which transfers similar loads without distortion – hence their universal use and survival from the Middle Ages to the present day.

The cause – or causes – of buckling should be correctly identified and remedial work proposed under architectural guidance. Releading will only be necessary if the leads have actually failed. Deformed panels can often be gently flattened and re-installed with additional support. Replacement tie-bars should be non-ferrous or have non-ferrous tips.

The loss of paint or enamel

The loss of paint and/or enamel can be caused by underfiring, the use of borax as a reducer of the melting point at which the paint fused onto the surface, inadequate flux preventing the enamel from adhering to the glass surface properly, chemical or abrasive cleaning either on or in the vicinity of the glass, or storage of the glass in an unsuitable environment.

Details of the surfaces should be recorded photographically – preferably in both colour and black and white using both transmitted and surface light. This should be done by your specialist glazier who will report on the causes of the problem and propose a solution which does not involve either the refiring or repainting of the glass.

Replacing lost paint on a backplate is appropriate only where a few important elements of the design are affected. It can be used selectively for faces, hands and other major features of the design, but is too expensive and heavy to use for all painted areas. It is a reversible method. Isothermal glazing (see below p.38) is advised for more extensive areas of paint loss or for total failure. This solution is a 'holding operation' to ensure no further loss through condensation, temperature extremes, weathering action etc. Sometimes the only viable solution to the problem is to record and leave.

There is no current reversible technique for fixing loose paint.

Organic growth on glass

Glass surfaces which are covered in weathering products, or are scuffed, or whose paint has a rough surface, appear to encourage the growth of disfiguring lichens, algae or fungi. This is especially notable on the north side of buildings or on glass which is sheltered from extremes of temperature and shaded from exposure to direct sun – although exceptions to these circumstances have been observed. It has been suggested that the rough surface of the glass provides both for anchorage for the rhizomes of the organisms and for the retention of surface moisture which reduces dessication of the organism.

Such surfaces should be cleaned extremely carefully without damaging any loose paint on either surface. Only neutral-pH soap available from conservator suppliers should be used. Chemical cleaners, especially hydrofluoric acid, must never be used. Any biocide which is used must be 'safe' for all the materials with which it will come into contact. The selection of a suitable biocide is a professional matter for your architect. (For details of currently available treatments, see *Practical Building Conservation* Volume 1, Chapter 2. Bibliography p.55.) Cleaning historic glass is a specialist operation.

Cracking, crazing or fissuring and fire damage

When the surface of glass is broken, the matrix of the whole structure disintegrates and various types of cracking, crazing or fissuring occur. This can be due to atmospheric attack, exposure to high temperature in a fire – or damage from misdirected directional heating devices.

The depth and extent of the crazing should be determined. If it is found to be superficial, the surface should be investigated for the application of a chemical or plastic coating or varnish at a previous time which may have failed or become damaged by heat or light. Characteristic crizzling combined with sugary opacity can be the result of too much alkali in the making of the glass. If the surface is sticky to the touch and exudes moisture, the glass was made with excessive potash as the alkali agent, and the surface is now composed of potassium carbonate which is hygroscopic and attracts and retains moisture.

The need for a specialist glazier's report to determine the exact cause and form of deterioration should be discussed with your architect. The solution may simply be to divert directional heating, or relocate a bonfire area outside the building. If the cause is failure of a chemical or plastic coating, this must be identified before any attempt is made to remove it. If fire damage is the cause, expert advice should be sought immediately. Fire crazing usually results in complete disintegration of the glass as soon as any dismantling of the cames is undertaken. No attempt should be made to touch or clean the surface of the glass however smoke-blackened it may be. A glass conservator should examine it and determine the extent of the damage so as to devise the best way to protect and remove it for conservation, if this is possible. Badly damaged and failed potash 'sugar' glass should be recorded *in situ* before replacement. It is not advisable to use either sticky tape or any proprietary brand of glue to consolidate crazed glass, as these can create more problems than they solve and are not always reversible or removable without extensive damage.

In some extreme cases where all of these signs of severe distress and deterioration are present, there is no known solution.

Shattered glass – shotgun or missile damage

A window which has inadequate exterior protection may be shattered by accidental damage, deliberate vandalism, stones flying up from lawn mowers, branches of trees or powerful winds.

In the event of such damage, every fragment from the broken window should be collected and loose or unsupported pieces that subsequently fall should be removed. Whenever possible, the original position of the pieces should be noted. This is where your photographic record will prove invaluable. Sticky tape or proprietary glues should not be applied. All collected broken pieces should be retained for the conservator. The damage should itself be photographed for the insurance assessor's scrutiny. If possible, a photographic enlargement of any damaged area should be provided from your photographic records to assist the conservator. The insurance company, police and your architect may all need to be informed – as well as the Archdeacon or DAC Secretary to advise on a faculty. Branches or bushes that threaten to beat against the glass should be cut back. Stones should be removed before mowing in the vicinity of vulnerable glazing. Missiles such as piles of stones or bricks should not be left to tempt vandals. Architectural advice should be sought on appropriate protective glazing or mesh (see below p.25). If vandalism is persistent, the police should be consulted on deterrent lighting, pressure pad alarm systems, restricting access, surveillance etc.

Water penetration

Water will penetrate glazing if the cementing medium between the cames and glass has failed, there are gaps in the glazing groove at the edge of the glass resulting from the failure of the mortar or the edge flanges of the lead panels, the overlap of the lead flanges between panels is inadequate or if the glass is cracked. Condensation on the inside of glass can be another source of excessive water (see below). Observation of a window during a period of rain can often reveal how water is penetrating. If no obvious cause of penetration is discernible, architectural advice should be sought. The window will require reglazing if it has to be releaded, re-weather proofed or re-cemented. Depending on the extent and seriousness of the damage, most of the other faults can be rectified *in situ* by an experienced glazier, but it is he who should advise on the correct degree and method of repair. Rags or gobbets of putty should not be used to block holes, plastic or sticky tape should not be stuck onto broken glass and proprietary brands of filler or sealant should not be used to stop leaks.

Condensation

Condensation is a deposit of moisture from the air onto the surface of the glass which occurs when the temperature of the glass is below the dew point temperature of the air. The diagnosis of the cause of the condensation is not always straightforward (for details see *Practical Building Conservation* Volume 2, Chapter 1). Significant factors are often the water vapour in people's breath, moisture-emitting heat sources, the pattern of heating cycles, insufficient ventilation, the outside air temperature (seasonal changes) and the orientation and thermal mass of the building.

Appropriate remedial action of the rectification of a condensation problem may be as simple as improving ventilation or changing an unsuitable heating system.

THE CLEANING OF GLASS

Every method devised for cleaning glass, including water and gentle brushing, can be damaging if the condition of the glass or paint is fragile or unstable. Before deciding upon a particular cleaning method, your conservator should make a detailed examination of both surfaces of the glass. It is important that the reasons why a particular cleaning method is selected is recorded. Secrecy, and the use of secret recipes can damage both the glass and the conservator's reputation. Do ask to visit the workshop and see your glass actually being conserved. It is sometimes helpful for fund-raising to ask your conservator to give an illustrated talk in the parish, or to help you to present a small exhibition with photographs of the conservation in progress for you to display in your church.

It is important to remember that nearly all the glass-cleaning techniques currently in use are at an experimental stage. Many have actually accelerated the rate of decay on the glass on which they were used and have created more problems than they solve in the short term. Controversy and criticism from glass conservators and technologists surround virtually every current cleaning process.

Cleaning methods to be avoided

Do not use any form of cleaning if loose paintwork or enamel has been detected on either the interior or the exterior of the glass. The best course of action in this instance is immediate recording, assessment of the cause of the loss and detailed discussion with your professional advisers – glazier and architect – on a preferred strategy.

Detergents, bleaches, caustic sodas, ammonia and acids (especially hydrofluoric acid), however diluted, must not be used. If any of these cleaning agents are to be used on either the window frame or the walls adjacent to the glass, the glass must be protected completely. The use of any proprietary brands of paint stripper on the glass should always be forbidden.

Whole panels of glass should never be removed by non-glaziers. Even when removed professionally they should never be immersed in chemical baths to free the cames from the mortars or putties holding them in place. Skilled conservators only have the experience to judge whether or not a panel and its painted glass is actually stable enough to saturate.

Any method of cleaning which scrapes or scratches the surface of the glass is to be avoided. All scratching and scuffing however minute, accelerates the development of pitting and corrosion wherever the surface of the glass has been damaged. Mechanical methods such as abrasive blasting, power tools and abrasive pads should never be used.

Cleaning with airbrasive, ultrasonic, lasers or dental drills should never be attempted by unskilled operators.

Glass should never be left unprotected if the building facade is to be cleaned.

The surface of cleaned glass and cames should never be coated with any type of 'protective' varnish or sealant.

If you are in any doubt about whether or not you should attempt to clean your glass, do nothing to it. Consult your architect as to whether it would be appropriate or advisable to undertake surface cleaning and, if so, what to use. Unpainted glass of any period and stable nineteenth-century glass which has no loose paint can be cleaned by gently brushing off cobwebs and dust followed by water – warm water is easier – applied with sponge or soft cloth. Do not press hard against the surface of the glass or you may deform or damage glass and lead.

Professional approaches to the removal of dirt and corrosion products

Over the years considerable sums of money have been spent on research establishing the nature of the corrosion of historic glass, but little has been spent on finding appropriate methods actually to clean

Dirty plain glazing disfigures both the exterior and interior of a church. Simple and regular cleaning of all plain glazing should be a normal part of the maintenance and care of a church – as it is with a car or a domestic dwelling. (Note the diagonal interior tie bar.)
Photo: J Kerr.

19

and conserve it. As a result there exists an extensive bibliography on the mechanisms of all aspects of glass corrosion and the analysis of the chemical or organic composition of corrosion products but virtually no information on how best to remove and prevent the corrosion recurring. (See the Bibliography p.55 for further reading.) This lack of knowledge places a heavy burden of responsibility on the conservator to use his skill and experience on the bench to determine the most appropriate methods to use and the extent of cleaning to undertake. As with almost all conservation work, the removal of dirt and corrosion products is a question of degree: the degree of the tenacity of the surface accretions and the degree of effectiveness of progressively interventionist methods deployed to remove it. It should never be forgotten that glass is a two-sided medium, and detailed examination of the nature and extent of the dirt and corrosion on both surfaces is essential before any work commences. Removal of any surface accretions should never damage any paint, enamel, washes or stain. Some surfaces can be easily cleaned *in situ*, others require the whole panel to be deglazed, dismantled and each individual piece of glass painstakingly cleaned by hand under a microscope to ensure the delicate paint lines are not lost. Details of appropriate cleaning methods currently in use are given in *Practical Building Conservation* Volume 5, Chapter 2.

THE REPAIR OF GLASS

Treatment of paint loss

There are only two reversible methods of dealing with paint loss at present: cold paint and back plating.

Cold paint (polymers, acrylics, water or oil based pigments) can really only be used effectively in ideal museum conditions where temperature changes are minimal, there is no threat of condensation, monitoring is easy and the glass can be removed for further care the moment any alteration occurs. This technique should never be used on *in situ* historically important glass.

Back plating is the only acceptable method in use for recovering the legibility of historically important glass. Details of the advantages and disadvantages of this method are given below on pp.36-38.

20

Total replacement

This should only be undertaken by your glazier in consultation with a glass historian. In the case of reverse or repeat cartoons, architectural designs, inscriptions or heraldry where it is quite clear what the design of the missing portion should be, this is relatively uncontroversial. For heads, hands and attributes it is more problematic. In principle this method of increasing the legibility of the window is reversible. Proper recording and the retention of the pieces of glass that are removed are as essential as inscribing the replacement pieces with the artist's name and the date.

Cracks and edge mending

The choice of method can only properly be resolved by the expert conservator on the bench. It is possible, for example, to remove disfiguring mending leads from important design features which can transform the legibility of the window and greatly improve the aesthetic appreciation and accessibility of the artist's original intention. Full details of the techniques currently in use are given in *Practical Building Conservation* Volume 5, Chapter 2.

SPECIAL CONSERVATION PROBLEMS

Plain glazing

Handmade plain glazing is greatly undervalued and is becoming the most threatened species of all types of historical glazing. The intrinsic importance of the variations of lucency, colour, form and design of this beautiful transformation of light into a building are yet to be fully appreciated.

It is lamentable that so much of this unique antique plain glazing has been replaced with characterless modern machine-made white glass. Modern glass in no way replicates the variation in hue, range of tone, surface movement and light-bending properties of hand-made glass. The whole appearance of the exterior of a church as well as the interior atmosphere can be entirely altered and diminished by the destruction of the exceptional effect of light passing through or reflected from original fifteenth-, sixteenth-, seventeenth- or eighteenth-century plain glazing. Where original plain glazing survives, it should be

Sixteenth-century historic plain glazing with original ferramenta (iron work) in the left and central light. The right light has been wholly replaced with modern plain diamond quarries. Note the flat, lifeless appearance, the disregard of the relationship between the original ferramenta and the panel divisions and the scale and proportions of the flat lead – all of which are inappropriate, unhistoric and demonstrate an erosion of original features and loss of originality.
Photo: J Kerr.

retained, preserved, mended and re-used and its life extended as long as possible. Some specialist glaziers have extensive stocks of this valuable resource, built up from purchasing discarded unregarded hand-made glass asset stripped or uncaringly removed from its context and sometimes even sold off for cullet. Their loss can be your gain. It is very important that the texture and type of replacement glazing for missing portions should be carefully matched. Now that window glass is no longer hand-made commercially anywhere in Britain, enterprising Continental glass manufacturers are reviving the techniques to meet an increasing demand for this special material. It is very unfortunate that in Britain this demand does not exist in commercially viable volume for a single British manufacturer to reinstate the handmaking of glass.

To safeguard the future of your historic plain glazing, ensure that your glazier and your architect are made fully aware of the importance you attach to the retention of as much as is technically possible of the original glass. Beware of such dangerously unspecific terms as 'reglaze', 'reform', 'replace' or 'repair as new'. It is perfectly practicable for an experienced and careful glazier to repair and reconstruct the characteristic irregularities of pre-nineteenth-century plain glazing patterns by the simple expedient of taking a lead rubbing of every individual panel before dismantling the glass, and then numbering each piece of glass on the glass itself and the rubbing so that each can be reglazed into its original position. It is important too to ensure that the same width of lead is used in the releading as in the original so that the proportional relationship and size of each panel remains the same after releading as before. Any replacement pieces can be cut to size using the lead rubbing as a cartóon. Unfortunately, it is much easier for the glazier to run up a completely new window with wholly modern flat glass than to trouble to retain all the irregularities and thus the character of the original. It is up to you, as custodians of this important and rare asset, to ensure that it is clear to all involved in the process of its removal for repair and replacement that you place great value on the retention and reinstatement of the original plain glazing.

Features to look out for and to record in your plain glazing are inscriptions on lead or diamond cut into the glass surface, the survival of pieces of horn and the use of pattern-stamped lead grilles glazed in for ventilation. All these unusual features should be preserved and re-used.

There is also an increasing tendency to replace nineteenth-century reticulated plain quarry glazing with plain glazing of contemporary design. While there is nothing intrinsically objectionable in this break with tradition, it should be remembered that there were actually sound practical reasons why diamond quarry glazing was used so ubiquitously and survived so extensively from earlier periods. It was an inexpensive, practical and successful solution to maximising light and glass because it held together without distortion. As explained above (p.21) when fixed correctly, the interactive network of glass and lead of diamond quarry glazing ensures that the combined and considerable weight of glass and lead in the glazing interspace is carried evenly from top to bottom without stress. Replacement designs based on small squares set in grids do not possess this structural efficiency and can suffer distortion resulting in a ziz-zag weakening of the infrastructure, the rapid opening up of the lead flanges holding the glass through vertical pressure and the eventual failure of the window as a water-tight entity. This can happen in a surprisingly short space of time and invariably requires expensive reglazing or replacement.

Glazing is an important design feature of both the interior and the exterior of your church. The removal of historic plain glazing will not only affect the quality of light to the interior and the appearance of the whole of the glazed opening, but can also have a detrimental effect on the external appearance of the entire church. It need hardly be said that the installation of any of the proprietary pressed glasses, double glazing units, moulded patterned glass or plate glass with superficial appliqué diamond quarry design across one surface are wholly inappropriate to historic buildings – especially churches. Remember that all reglazing and deglazing, replacements and redesigns require faculty permission and so early consultation with your DAC is essential and a faculty should be obtained before you enter into any commitment.

Appliqué glass

This is a twentieth-century technique which combines different coloured plastics and glasses applied in varying layers of colour and tonal density to a base glass. The panels have no lead but are constructed of sandwiches of glue, glass and plastic. The effect of such intense colour can be very exciting. However, recently many of these compositions have shed sherds and have had to be replaced or repaired. The difficulty appears to have been the failure of the glue to flex with the thermal movement of the glass as it expands and contracts in response to temperature fluctuations. There are also indications that if epoxy resins were used these have suffered from ultra-violet degradation. In some cases water has caused damage by penetrating between the adhesive and the glass itself. At present there does not appear to be a solution to this built-in obsolescence. As many of the original designers are still practising, the British Society of Master Glass Painters (address on p.54) can help you to trace the original artist.

Dalles de verre

This is also a twentieth-century technique where problems of structural failure have occurred. Again the BSMGP may be able to assist you in locating the original designer. This type of design is constructed from thick slabs of cast glass faceted and chipped and set into concrete or epoxy/cement mixtures. Failure occurs when metal cramps set in the cement rust and spall, damaging the glass and the integrity of the structure. There have also been failures of combinations of glass fibres, glass slabs and the resin/concrete mixes where the damage is caused by thermal behaviour differentials between the different materials and, in some cases, the penetration of water.

EXTERNAL PROTECTION

There are two main reasons for installing external protection:

a) to preserve the glass from damage by vandals or accidental breakage;

b) to protect conserved or fragile glass from the weather, atmospheric attack or extreme fluctuations of temperature.

a) Protection from vandalism or accidental breakage

Some insurance companies (including the Ecclesiastical Insurance Group) recommend exterior protection of important stained glass, and can specify the degree of protection required. There are several types of protection currently in use. The relative merits and disadvantages of these are discussed in the following sections.

All types of external protection must be fitted within the framework of the main light and tracery panels to preserve the overall appearance of

Wire mesh fitted directly to the outer frame of the whole window. Experts can cut and finish mesh to fit within the shape of the main lights and tracery avoiding overlaps such as here at the shoulder of the light which can detach and encourage birds to nest between the glass and the mesh. Photo: J Kerr.

the window. They should never be fitted across the whole exterior of a window. All fixings should be non-ferrous and be caulked with lead. They should never be pointed round with mastic or mortar. Percussive drills should never be used to create the holes for fixings. Fixings should be made into joints between masonry units or, if this is quite impossible, so that only one unit adjacent to a joint is affected. THIS IS A PROFESSIONAL JOB WHATEVER METHOD IS USED. Your architect should always be consulted to specify the fixing and subcontract the work to a professional. A faculty will always be required for this work so early consultation with the Diocesan Advisory Committee is essential.

1 WIRE GUARDS

When firmly fixed in place, these can deflect missiles but not shotgun pellets. Unprotected iron wire or mesh guards should not be used as even galvanized meshes when cut to shape will corrode at the cut

Virtuoso, expert, wire cutting. Specialists can cut and shape wire guards to fit within the most complex architectural forms. These tracery light guards have been carefully designed by the architect so that the symmetry of the strengthening bars reflects the rhythm of the stonework. The specification has ensured the plastic coating matches the tone of the stonework.
Photo: J Kerr.

Metal frame fixed over the entire window with no alignment or relationship to the stone framework of the window itself. The flimsy mesh within the frame is not stretched and fixed with sufficient tension to resist a large missile. Maximum disfigurement resulting in minimum protection. Photo: J Kerr.

ends. Wire mesh grilles should be made by skilled wire-workers to accurate templates provided by glaziers and galvanized *after* fabrication. They should be fixed by glaziers. A thicker wire frame around each guard is also important.

Advantages

- The exterior of the glass is fully exposed to the cleaning action of wind and rain.
- They are relatively inexpensive.
- They are easy to cut to templates designed to match the shapes of window openings and tracery lights.
- They are easy to remove for cleaning, deglazing, stone repair and replacement.
- They do not involve any adjustment to the infrastructure of the window for fixing.
- If plastic-coated galvanised mesh is used, it can be colour matched to the surrounding stone and is therefore less visually obtrusive. Dark colours have been used with particular success.

Conventional iron wire guard. Unpainted and unmaintained, the wires have rusted irreversibly staining the stonework with a weeping red sill mark. Copper mesh can also corrode creating a green stain in stonework which is equally disfiguring and indelible. The eroded and rusted grille no longer protects the glass and has seriously damaged the building.
Photo: J Kerr.

Disadvantages

- Copper or iron wires should not be used as the corrosion and rust will eventually stain and disfigure the masonry fabric below the window. Such stains are either impossible or very expensive to remove.
- They do not deter persistent vandals using heavy missiles or guns.
- They can be bent back or broken to permit a break-in.
- They are clearly visible from the interior and can create a visually disfiguring grid pattern across the design of the glass.
- If they are not properly maintained and fixed, birds can build nests between the glass and the guard.
- They need maintenance and renewal at regular intervals.

2 PLASTIC SHEETING

Plastics are becoming more frequently used. There are currently two types on the market: acrylics (such as Perspex and Oroglass) and polycarbonates (such as Lexan).

Advantages
- They are relatively inexpensive and easily obtained.
- They provide greater impact resistance than wire guards, and can even deflect shotgun pellets if a thick enough sheet is used.
- They provide complete coverage of the glazing area.
- A specialist fitter can cut the plastic to fit the shapes of the window openings very closely.
- They act as draught excluders and the air cavity increases the thermal insulation.
- They are relatively light in weight compared to glass sheets.
- They are flexible and can accommodate external ferramenta.
- If properly fixed or set within a fixing frame, they can be removed for easy access to the glass or repairs to the stone.
- Polycarbonate sheeting can be subdivided horizontally with lead cames corresponding to saddle bars to give an appropriate external pattern and reduce distorted reflections.

Disadvantages

- All plastic sheeting is highly flammable. As fire is such an effective destroyer of glass, plastics should never be used to protect ancient glass or glass of high quality where the exterior is accessible to vandals.

Glass fibre based plastic sheeting which has become totally opaque through exposure to sunlight over a period of just five years. The interior is now completely dark – even in broad daylight. Inexpertly fitted, cut and fixed in neat cement, the sheets are very difficult to remove and have a wholly unacceptable detrimental effect on both the exterior and interior of the church. Photo: J Kerr.

- All plastics gradually surface-craze and take on a milky appearance and lose lucency through exposure to sunlight and through chemical loss.
- Acrylics are more easily scratched than polycarbonates, but both are subject to surface scuffing and etching which is not reversible, and which accelerates the deterioration of the translucency.
- Lichens, moulds and dirt easily accumulate on any surface scratches.
- The sheets MUST be removed at regular intervals so that the glass can be washed, insect activity cleaned off (especially spiders' webs) and the ferramenta properly maintained.
- They are often installed without ventilation which eventually leads to damage to the glass fabric and lead panel behind.
- Inexpert cutting causes rapid deterioration of the edges or 'star-crazing' around the holes drilled for fixing which frequently results in cracking.

Proprietary plastic sheets screwed in place and inexpertly fitted in such a way as to encourage birds to roost at the apex of the window. The excrement is not cleaned off by the action of wind and rain but etched into the surface where it remains damaging the visual appearance of the church exterior and the interior effect of the stained glass it 'protects'. Note the sheets are not cut to size and have unsightly overlaps.
Photo: J Kerr.

- Plastic panels must be fixed to allow for expansion and contraction in response to temperature fluctuation, otherwise the sheets can buckle, crack, fissure and even detach themselves from the fixings.
- They MUST always be ventilated top and botton to allow for the free passage of air. If this is not done, then condensation will occur and damage the glass and lead. Condensation also provides a microclimate suitable for algae and lichens to form.
- Although they do not intrude upon the legibility of the glass from the interior until their increasing opacity begins to reduce the light level, the effect on the exterior elevation of flat, reflective sheets can often be disastrous.
- Birds often use the top of plastic sheets to perch or to nest on, and their excrement etches into the surface of all plastics.
- If inadequately fixed, winds can penetrate behind the sheeting and remove the sheets by leeward suction, damaging both the glass and its setting.
- The aesthetic effect on the exterior of tr.e church can be disastrous.

3 GLASS SHEETS

Glass reinforced by wire mesh has been in use since 1898, when it was developed to meet the demand for safety precautions in skylights, roofing and fire doors. It has the advantage of holding together when damaged or broken by impact or heat, but can be fractured by shot and will star craze. It is made with normal sands which give the glass a green tint. Laminated, toughened, plain, cast and plate glasses have all been used to protect stained glass for decades – indeed some have been in place since the middle of the last century. Laminated glass free from the iron oxide that causes greenishness is obtainable. It is relatively expensive but probably provides the highest quality of glass sheet protection.

Advantages

- The exterior is easy to clean.
- The covering of the opening is complete so it acts as double glazing to improve heat retention.
- Visual intrusion on the interior effect of the design is minimal.
- It acts as a deterrent to thieves intent upon breaking in.
- If completely and correctly sealed within the window frame it reqires no maintenance apart from cleaning.
- It protects the glass within from most forms of vandal attack by presenting a defensive layer that can be sacrificed and replaced.

Plastic sheets tightly fitted within the framework of the window design. Although cut to shape, the sheets are flexed to fit the main lights in such a way that the distorting effect of the reflection subverts the external integrity of the fenestration. The plastic is also so tightly fitted that it is unventilated and will present removal difficulties when it has decayed to opacity from exposure to sunlight.
Photo: J Kerr.

Disadvantages

- All forms of external sheet glass are extremely visually obtrusive and change the external appearance of the building.
- For fixing, a glazing groove has often to be cut or widened in the architectural frame which may irrevocably damage the moulding and proportions of the window.
- It is not easily removed for repair, cleaning, or maintenance of either glass or metal fittings.
- It cannot easily be used where external ferramenta are present.
- If fractured or broken, the whole sheet has to be replaced.
- It is difficult to examine the condition of the exterior of the glass it protects.
- Overglazing fixed without lead came edgings to accommodate differential thermal movement between the glass and the fixing mortar or masonry may permit water penetration. This in turn may lead to condensation problems, mould growth and the collection of water between the glazing.

A sheet of glass cemented against the window it 'protects'. The lack of ventilation has allowed condensation to collect in the interspace, lichen is growing on both surfaces and the glass cannot be easily removed for cleaning or for the removal of the broken pane which has slipped into the interspace (bottom right). Both the interior and the exterior aesthetic effect are disastrous.
Photo: J Kerr.

35

- If it is totally sealed into the mullions, moisture may be drawn from within the building through the joints of cames.
- Tiny insects can collect and breed in the glazed interspace. These cannot be controlled or removed without removing the entire sheet.
- If there is no outlet at the base, water can collect sandwiched between the glass, disfiguring and damaging both interfaces.

b) Protection of conserved or fragile glass from weather, atmospheric attack and extreme fluctuations of temperature

There are four systems in use by conservators: backplating of individual pieces of glass, isothermal double glazing, external protective glazing, and chemical coatings. All of these should be installed by the workshop which cleans and conserves the glass and should never be carried out by a separate contractor.

1 BACKPLATING

When an individual piece of glass is broken and requires extensive edge-mending, either by silica-based glues or copper foiling – or a combination of both – and the conserved glass is not to be protected overall by external glazing, a conservator will strengthen the mended glass by glazing a backplate to the exterior. This is set within the same lead came as the mended piece, and should be completely weatherproofed. (The process is discussed above on page 13.)

Advantages

- The process is totally reversible.
- Where there are missing pieces of the design, the legibility of the whole can be restored by painting and firing the missing portions of the design onto the backing plate.
- If the conserved glass is very thin or fragile, it extends its life since it is no longer functioning to keep out the weather, and is not subject to the same degree of stress due to temperature fluctuations.
- If fragments of the original conserved glass are missing, small replacements can be added to complete the whole within the same lead, thus preserving the integrity of the design.
- The original cut-line can be restored even if the broken piece has been subsequently grozed to take a mending lead.
- Later insertions which are obtrusive or inappropriate can be recorded and removed for replacement by more sympathetic or neutral glass.

36

- The conservation and repair of single pieces of glass by backplating is often all that is required – for example, roundels, heraldic devices, faces, inscriptions, enamelled glass etc.
- If the original intensity of the colour of the glass has been greatly reduced by the removal of corrosion or the loss of flashing or the intrinsic thickness of the pot metal, then coloured backplating can restore the lost dimension.
- Yellow stain is almost invariably applied to the exterior surface of glass and has frequently been lost or destroyed by weathering or chemical cleaning. This design detail can be replaced on a backplate to the exact dimensions of the original by following the surviving paint line of the interior painted design.
- Missing or destroyed backpainting can be replaced on the backplate.
- All such restorations of detail, design or colour can be clearly recorded, and all backplates signed and dated. This is usually done on the edge where it is concealed by the lead flange and is therefore instantly discernible by subsequent conservators.
- If anything goes wrong with the conserved glass, it can be deglazed, examined and rectified using the backing plate for support.

Disadvantages

- Some conservators using this technique frequently glued the glass to be conserved on to the backing plate. This has caused a lot of damage. It is especially difficult to reverse, as in most cases individual recipes of animal glues were used and no records were kept.
- Early twentieth-century conservators used completely flat glass for the backing plate. As medieval glass is never completely flat, they cut up the original glass so as to make it easier to stick to the flat backplate, thus damaging the glass further.
- The backplating must be completely sealed against the glass it is protecting. This is done by making a mould from the exterior of the piece to be protected into which the backplate is shaped in the kiln. The backplate is sealed with the protected glass by mastic within the lead. If this is not done, a micro-climate is created which can damage the conserved glass.
- The use of extensive or numerous backing plates increases the overall weight of the panel, and may require additional support for the structure from integrated ferramenta or tie bars.
- Inexpertly integrated backing plates with inadequate leads or

putty/mastic sealant place the protected glass at risk. They should be removed and replaced properly as soon as possible after the deficiency is noticed. Adhesive tape or proprietary glues must never be used on the interior painted surface.

2. ISOTHERMAL DOUBLE GLAZING

This system has been in use since the 1950s. The principle is to remove the conserved glass from direct exposure to the elements and to place it within the envelope of the building where the temperature of the glass is the same on both sides. This is achieved by removing the conserved glass from the original fixing frame or glazing groove, which is then glazed completely with modern white glass, cut and leaded to follow the main outlines of the design of the original panel it will protect. In some cases, a simpler system of single sheets of glass with the surface transformed by relaxing it in the kiln to give it life and movement approximate to hand-made glass – and thus less visually intrusive to the exterior of the church, can be used. In both systems, the original conserved glass is then inserted on a new interior frame specially constructed for the purpose, fixed within the mullions and ventilated all around to the interior of the building. This system is designed to eliminate condensation because the interior and exterior surfaces of the conserved glass are in an isothermal environment – that is, they are at the same temperature within the building, and no longer subject to the extreme fluctuations of temperature created by the exposure to interior and exterior differentials.

Advantages

- If the building is properly ventilated, the conserved glass is not subjected to any condensation and experiences only minimal disturbances from changes in temperature and humidity.
- This system can help insulate the building from heat loss.
- The condition of both surfaces of the conserved glass can be easily monitored by simply removing each panel from its fixing within the frame.
- Access for any further conservation, cleaning or exhibition purposes is easy.
- If the method of following the main lines of the design and panel division for the cut lines of the external glazing is used, there is minimal visual disturbance from the interior due to parallax, and the exterior elevation is not detrimentally affected.
- The conserved glass is not replaced into the same atmospheric

conditions that may originally have accelerated or caused the advancement of decay and deterioration in the first instance.

- If minimal conservation has been carried out, the conserved glass is effectively in an environment consistent with a 'holding operation'. This is especially important in cases where there are no present solutions to particular problems – such as paint loss resulting from the 'borax' problem or under firing – and where continual exposure to condensation and extremes of temperature places the glass at risk.

- This system of protection should extend the life of the glass until solutions are developed for problems which cannot be dealt with in the current state of knowledge, and at least will ensure that there is something left to conserve when solutions are eventually found. It is arguable that this system of 'moth-balling' the problem is preferable to experimenting with techniques that have yet to be proved effective, and which are, in the main, not reversible.

Disadvantages

- This is the most expensive solution of all because of the additional cost of constructing the interior frame to hold the conserved glass.
- In order to eliminate halation around the re-set, conserved panels, it is necessary for a light-excluding border to be glazed around the outer edges of each panel. This increases the cost, but decreases the vulnerability of the conserved glass at its weakest point.
- The glazing interspace determines the amount of ventilation between the two surfaces. If it is too small, the passage of air is restricted, while if the space is too large, the effect on the proportions of the interior mouldings can be unsatisfactory. It is essential that the architect be fully involved with the design and dimensions of the fixings and the frame to avoid these difficulties.
- The exterior glazing does not always effectively protect the glass from attack by vandals, and it may still require the additional installation of wire guards.
- It is essential that the building is properly ventilated. If it is not, condensation can still occur on the conserved surfaces.
- For security it is necessary for the conserved glass to be firmly fixed in position.
- If the new glass installed in the exterior glazing groove does not have a leaded design modelled on the design and panel divisions of the conserved glass, the lead pattern will disfigure the interior effect of the original. If a plain sheet is used, it is the exterior architecture which suffers.

The conserved glass remains in its original glazing groove, and the protective modern glazing is inserted outside it. As the interspace is ventilated to the exterior of the building, the conserved glass is still subjected to the extremes of temperature from without and within, although it is protected from having to serve to keep the elements out.

Advantages

- The conserved glass does not have to have a specially constructed frame and remains in its original groove.
- There is no halation problem from the edges of the conserved glass.
- This system is therefore cheaper than the isothermal glazing as fewer modifications to the existing arrangements are necessary.
- The conserved glass does not have to be weathertight.
- Condensation is reduced.
- The integrity of the interior mouldings and proportions are retained.

Disadvantages

- The whole of the exterior glazing has to be removed to monitor and clean the exterior of the conserved glass unless it is properly hinged.
- The conserved glass is still subjected to exterior atmospheric pollution.
- The additional exterior glazing can create technical and aesthetic problems if the rebate must be widened or part of the exterior moulding lost to allow for fixing the new glazing into the stonework.
- There can still be extremes of temperature between the interior and the exterior of the conserved glass.

4 CHEMICAL COATINGS.

It is not yet posssible to be confident about the long-term performance and hence the protective value of synthetic coatings on historic glass. They are also controversial because they are not reversible. Most synthetic coatings require painstaking and time-consuming application to the exterior surface of each individual piece of cleaned glass before re-leading, and are therefore expensive as well.

In the past, various proprietary varnishes and early plastic 'colour enhancing' substances were used, often with disastrous long-term results. As the applied substance contracts and reacts differently to the glass, this early period of experimentation has resulted in surfaces discolouring, cracking, crizzling, shaling off with the paint lines – or even the entire surface of the glass. Cellulose nitrate plasticised with camphor (Celluloid) was one of the most damaging coatings quite widely used at the beginning of this century. It eventually formed a totally opaque layer, which contracted removing all the surface and any associated loose paint.

As records were rarely kept at this time, any supervening substance on the surface of the glass should be identified, and advice sought on its removal as further experimentation may only increase the damage. The Ancient Monuments Laboratory and the Research and Technical Advisory Service of English Heritage can advise on where analysis can be carried out and should be consulted in the event of any difficulty. CVMA Occasional Paper II (see Bibliography) contains an extensive and detailed bibliography on the subject of resin coatings (such as Viacryl), wax coatings, the Jacobi process, Hydrophobic and Monomolecular layers. The British Glass Manufacturers Confederation can provide an updated list of recent research papers.

At this time, chemical coatings are best not used at all.

CONCLUSIONS

There are no perfect solutions for the complete protection of glass. Each situation and problem is specific and must be individually assessed. By its very nature glass will always be vulnerable to breakage, damage and deterioration. All that can be done is to protect where possible, preserve where feasible and always keep photographic and written records.

41

GUIDELINES RECOMMENDED FOR THE PROTECTION OF HISTORICALLY IMPORTANT GLASS

The following guidelines are intended to assist those responsible for the protection and maintenance of historical glass. They are not exclusive to ecclesiastical buildings.

- Work to the fabric of most Church of England churches requires a faculty from the diocesan consistory court, except where the work is so minor that it is regarded as 'de minimis'; most work to glass, however, it likely to require a faculty. If you are in any doubt on procedure always check with your Archdeacon or Diocesan Advisory Committee Secretary before you put any work in hand.

- Assess the advantages and disadvantages of external systems before making your selection. The wrong choice for the wrong reason installed by the wrong person can irrevocably damage both the building and the glass which is to be protected.

- Always consult your architect on any proposals and seek his advice before fitting any form of external protection or engaging a specialist glazier. His professional involvement will protect you financially through a formal contracting agreement and will ensure the building is equally protected through his specification instructing glazier, mason and/or blacksmith accordingly.

- If you need additional advice, seek the views of your Diocesan Advisory Committee or consult the Council for the Care of Churches which has a specialist Stained Glass Advisory Committee. If you have received grant aid from English Heritage (or their predecessor, the Department of the Environment) they too can advise. Do not forget that a condition of their grants is that you notify English Heritage of any proposed future works. It may be that the work you are proposing is itself grant eligible.

- Ask your local authority conservation officer for names of other owners of historic buildings or church officials in your area with similar problems.

- Find out (from any of the above) where you can see local examples of the types of external protection under consideration so that you can judge the effect for yourself on both the glass and the building. It may also be useful to find out who did the installation, what sort of service they gave, and what those who use and look after the building think of the system.

- Consult your insurance company on their requirements for acceptable protective coverage.

- Consult the police if vandalism is persistent. They can advise on deterrent lighting, restricting access, alarm systems and surveillance.

- Notify the police of the location of particularly valuable glass so that it can be included on a patrol itinerary.

- Have all your vulnerable and important glass fully recorded photographically. The CVMA Archive at the National Monuments Record of the Royal Commission on Historical Monuments (England) can advise on this. Their address is on page 53.

- Seek architectural advice on the treatment or replacement of rusting or corroding guards that are staining the stonework.

- Remove all ivy and creeping plants from wire guards or the surface of any protective glazing.

- Ensure that fixings of any protective system cause minimum damage and are completely reversible.

- Engage the conservator and your architect in a proper system of 'after-care' surveillance and monitoring so that further problems can be detected and rectified before they become serious, damaging and expensive to deal with.

- Include proper maintenance of all types of external protection in a regular programme.

- Keep the external surface of plain or sheet glazing free of dirt, lichens, algae and mould by using an appropriate biocide.

- Monitor plastic sheets for cracking, crazing, the working loose of fittings, buckling or increasing opacity. Inform your architect of any developments or problems.

- Replace broken or failed external protection having first sought architectural advice and obtained a faculty.

- Ensure that at all times exterior protection is properly ventilated and that water collecting at the base will run out freely.

- Make sure that ventilation gaps and holes in any type of protective glazing are not blocked and have small mesh or grilles fixed to prevent further blockage and access for insects, small animals and birds.

- Remove birds' nests from any system of external protection and refix it properly to ensure that there is no recurrence.

- Do not select a protective system simply because it is cheap or can be done on a do-it-yourself basis. This approach invariably creates more problems than it solves and leaves those financially liable to rectify damage.

- Strenuously avoid ready-made commercial double glazing as it is wholly inappropriate for use on an ecclesiastical or historic building. The proportions, materials, detailing and installation are invariably unsatisfactory and damage to the fabric is expensive to rectify.

- It is well worth drawing the attention of the fire brigade officer to the locations of important historic glass to avoid its being smashed to provide access for firefighters in the event of a fire.

- Watch out for condensation and always ensure that your building is properly ventilated. Your architect can advise on any problems that arise.

- Prevent birds from perching on the top of any external protective system and damaging the surface with disfiguring droppings.

- Prune back any overhanging trees or bushes so that no damage can be done by branches beating against the glass or protective glazing and guards.

- Ask the conservator to write down his recommendations for methods of keeping the protective glazing or guards in good condition.

- Never leave any potential missiles lying about near important glass. Piles of bricks, stones, cobbles, rubbish etc. are temptation incarnate. Make sure that any specification for adjacent works or works to the building make this absolutely clear. Inform your architect that you wish this precaution included in any instruction to contractors or sub-contractors. If any damage results from their negligence you then have legal redress for the costs. Local authorities should also be watched if they are carrying out works in the vicinity. It is advisable to instruct them in writing that any damage to your glass resulting from their employees leaving throwable material or tools lying around is their financial liability.

- Never permit any chemical or other type of cleaning of your church without ensuring that the glass is to be fully protected. Make sure this is written into the contract for this or any other type of work that could involve damage to your glass by a careless contractor or operative. This is especially important for sand-blasting, any use of chemicals, high-pressure hoses, the erection of scaffolding etc. All such works should in any case be specified and carried out under your architect's supervision with a faculty.

- It is also important to ensure that your grass mower does not have the opportunity to throw up stones or gravel that could shatter or break your glass.

- Never use pressure hoses or steam cleaning on glass. This can destroy putty, mortar, fragile glass, friable paint, tired leadwork, insecure glass etc. Thousands of pounds' worth of damage can be done in seconds.

- Do not allow any chemicals, varnishes, sprays, acids or 'secret recipes' to be used on your glass for any reason. Always consult your architect.

- Never permit amateurs such as manpower services, youth training schemes, etc. to work on or near any historically important glass. Any damage they do – however closely supervised the work was – you will have to rectify entirely from your own pocket. Your insurance will not cover it if you have consented to the work, it is very difficult to claim damages from uninsured non-professionals and government-sponsored labour is Crown Exempt from prosecution.

- Do not hesitate to ask for professional advice on any aspect of exterior protection or glazing. It will always cost less than any damage that will ensue from an amateur approach and inadequate insurance coverage.

COMMISSIONING A NEW WINDOW

This can be a most exciting and a most exasperating experience for the donor, the parish and the designer alike. There are certain pitfalls to avoid and correct legal procedures to observe as well as the need to reconcile the wishes of the donor with the context in which the glass is to be placed. Aesthetic, practical, technical and architectural considerations must be weighed in the balance before even considering how to set about selecting a glass designer. It is helpful to address the answers to the following questions at the outset to avoid difficulties later on:

- What glass exists in the church already?

- Do any existing windows need conservation, releading or protection? If so, would the donor prefer to choose the extension of the life of an old and familiar friend rather than the introduction of a new work?

- Is a completely new window actually needed? Perhaps only a central light or the tracery of a window need be selected.

- Are there gaps in the present glazing which affect the spatial unity of the interior? It is sometimes more satisfying to complete a series than to introduce a new element into a unified programme.

- Should the subject matter be representational or abstract? If the former is preferred, is there any continuity of theme or subject with the present glazing programme?

- What are the cost limitations – how much can the donor afford?

- If only a small amount of money is available, would an innovative design in plain glazing be appropriate?

- What type of glazing would fit the atmosphere of the church?

- How would its external appearance affect the architectural aesthetics of the church?

- What colours, techniques, designs and styles would be compatible

46

with the existing glazing and appropriate to the architectural context?

• Will the end result involve the parish in expensive insurance costs, future conservation problems or difficulties in protecting the new window from vandals? These considerations are particularly important where sheets of engraved glass are concerned.

• Does the proposed location present problems technically – either in terms of the physical condition of the stone or brick into which the glass is to be fixed, or the difference the insertion of a stained glass window will make to the light level of the interior of the church?

• What is the external background to the window – for example, are there dark trees or adjacent buildings which already exclude the light?

• Will the insertion of a new window affect the present interior lighting system?

• What does the donor actually visualise? If this is incompatible with the answers to the above questions, the wishes of the PCC or the exigencies of the building itself, it would be well to discuss the differences and achieve a successful resolution BEFORE proceeding and involving any expense.

Clearly it is advisable to involve your architect at the earliest stage of discussion since he or she will have the answer to several of the above questions.

Choosing a designer

It is always advisable to consult your Diocesan Advisory Committee as soon as possible. Some DACs have specialist stained glass advisers. Many will be able to refer the PCC and the donor to both successful and unsuccessful examples of new commissions in the Diocese to help towards choosing both a compatible design and designer. Do not forget that in any case the PCC will need to obtain a faculty, not only for the insertion of the new window, but also for the removal of the old.

Sometimes your architect will be able to introduce you to stained glass designers he has worked with or whose work he knows. It is always desirable to go and see the work of any recommended designer actually in its architectural context, as it is notoriously difficult to assess the effect of the finished, luminous, glazed work *in situ* from an untranslucent, opaque, coloured drawing on paper. It may be helpful at this stage to form a small sub-committee – including the donor and, perhaps, the DAC specialist and your architect – to research the choice of a designer if no obvious candidate is immediately identifiable. Whether or not it is decided to form a sub-committee, I will address the commissioning agent as 'you' in the following text.

The Council for the Care of Churches has a collection of photographs which illustrates the recent work of stained glass artists and designers to help you to choose. The British Society of Master Glass Painters and the Worshipful Company of Glaziers of the City of London can also introduce you to the work of contemporary designers. Both these organisations can also advise on glass engravers and alternative techniques to stained glass. (Addresses are given at the end of this booklet, page 53). You may wish to consider giving a new home to glass from a redundant church, and in this case, the Stained Glass Repository of the Company of Glaziers may be able to meet your needs. All these organisations have small specialist libraries where you can consult publications illustrating the work of contemporary designers.

Today there are many combinations of artists working to produce designs, and you are sure to find one who is able to meet your needs. Sometimes the designer does not actually transfer his design to glass himself, but uses a separate firm of glaziers to translate his artistry into glass through their technical experience. You may prefer to commission an individual who does both the design work and the execution. It may also interest you to select a future genius for yourself from the Diploma Show at a College of Art. Again, the Glaziers Company Information Service can let you know the dates of these shows and give you the addresses of all the Colleges which teach window glass design.

How to proceed when you have selected your designer

Always draw up a precise brief to give all the details of what is required. This makes it quite clear what you are expecting and avoids disappointments and misunderstanding. Give the location, dimensions and context of the window. Your architect is invaluable at this stage in embodying your wishes in the form of a specification.

Measured drawings, photographs and historical details are particularly useful. Before proceeding any further, you can approach several artists with your specification at this stage and ask them to give you a list of their recent work and an indication of the cost of a commission. Always make it clear what the terms are on which you will be selecting the successful design – including whether or not you have approached other artists or whether it is a competition to be decided by judges. If you decide on the latter course, the British Society of Master Glass Painters can give you all the details of how to set about devising a competition, where to advertise, how much it will cost and what the appropriate rules are.

If you ask more than three artists to submit designs from which to make your final selection, this will involve you in additional expense. You can always ask one designer to submit several designs to you. As with all commissions of works of art, the donor pays for all the expense the artist incurs in the submission of designs – whether or not what is produced is finally selected to be carried out. Costs will vary according to the reputation of the artist, the size of the area to be glazed, the techniques to be used and the cost of the materials as well as the complexity of the design itself. The clearer you are in informing the artist of your requirements, the less cost you will incur in the preliminary stages. To prevent misunderstanding, always state at the outset what the fee you are paying for a preliminary sketch covers – whether or not it includes travel expenses to meet you and see the church, how many different designs you wish to see etc.

Once you have selected a design and a designer, you can ask the artist to develop or amend the design. You can also ask the artist to present the proposed design to the DAC for their approval. Once this is given and the faculty granted, the architect should also discuss the timescale with you all, especially if the installation involves any preliminary work by masons to repair or replace any of the architectural framework or if the metal support system for the glass requires redesigning. The architect should also advise on the taking out of the glazing to be superseded and on the fixing of the new window – especially the specification for the mortar mix for the edge of the glass where it meets the architectural framework.

Once all has been agreed it is essential to formalise all aspects of the procedure in a form of contract. The artist must be asked to give you an agreed price for the complete work and the PCC and the architect as well as the donor must all know the total financial commitment for the whole operation. The timescale should also be specified and it should also be quite clear precisely who is reponsible for each stage of the work. The artist must know which design is approved and with which amendments as well as when the completed work is required to be installed. It must be clear who is responsible for providing scaffolding, removing the glazing to be superseded, taking measurements and templates, disposing of the removed glass, insuring the new work, taking any photographs required, paying for visits, travel expenses, faculty charges (if still applicable), and the architect's fees. It should also be stated at the outset if the artist requires payment in instalments to help his cash flow in purchasing the raw materials.

Most artists like to take a very personal interest in all aspects of the commission and particularly value developing a relationship with the building, the donor and the parish. The whole enterprise can be a most fulfilling and rewarding experience for all concerned. Stained glass is a living tradition very close to and part of the whole historic development of the church and both its iconography and architecture. The commissioning and dedication of a new window focuses the whole parish on this continuity of patronage in the context of the church. It is often the only experience in a lifetime of the commissioning of a work of art and the patronage of an artist. It can be a considerable enhancement of appreciation of the architectural context of worship, its light and space, as well as an intrinsic spiritual inspiration.

GLOSSARY OF TERMS

'Antique' glass: Common term for hand-made glass blown by the 'muff' method (see below) and containing bubbles, ripples and irregularities.

Backpainting: Painting on the exterior surface of the glass.

Came: The strip of lead, H-shaped in cross-section, which is wrapped round the edge of the cut glass pieces to make up the design panels. The cames are joined by soldering, and the gaps between the flanges and the glass surface are filled with putty or mastic to prevent water penetration (see 'Cement').

Cartoon: Full-size design for a window complete with lead lines and detail to be painted.

Cathedral glass: Commercial name for machine rolled glass. NB this is a trade term only and has no relationship with cathedral glazing.

Cement: Technical glazing term which refers to putty or mastic filler between the glass and the cames which links them and makes the window waterproof.

Crizzling: The roughening, crumpling or scaling of the surface of glass which impairs its clarity. A form of decay and decomposition usually associated with fire damage.

Crown or spun glass: A bubble of molten glass which has been removed from the pot in the furnace is blown to increase its size, shaped into a pear-like form, and then cut open at one end and spun on a pontil rod so that the centrifugal force flares the glass out to form a flat disc. This always has a thicker centre where the pontil rod was attached, sometimes known as a 'bull's eye' or 'bullion'. This part was usually cut out and sold off cheaply as waste as its density diminished its transparency. The current vogue for inept, moulded or pressed imitations of bullions for domestic and 'character' commercial glazing is a travesty of the original form and vivid plasticity of the authentic bullion.

CVMA: Corpus Vitrearum Medii Aevi.

Dalles de verre: Thick slabs of glass produced by casting in moulds. As the slabs are too thick for retention in lead, they are set in concrete or resin and chipped or faceted to the required shape (twentieth century).

Ferramenta: The iron framework or fittings which provide a fixing for panels within a wide window space. The panels are held in the frame by triangular metal pegs inserted into lugs on the main frame.

51

The design of the ferramenta is an integral feature of the panel arrangement.

Flash: A thin coat of coloured glass applied ('flashed') to the surface of white or pot-metal glass during manufacture. The flashing can be abraded or removed by acid to reveal the colour of the base glass, achieving two tones on the same piece of glass, a technique frequently used in heraldry. Red or ruby glass is commonly flashed.

Glazing bar: A horizontal or vertical T-shaped support for panels of glass in large openings. The glass rests on the T-shaped profile. Sometimes called a T-bar.

Grisaille: Geometric or leaf patterns of regular design leaded into or painted on white glass. (From the French *grisailler*, to paint grey.)

Grozing: The medieval method of shaping glass by means of a metal tool with a hooked end which made a characteristic bitten edge. (Post-medieval glass is cut by a diamond or sharp metal tool, which creates a straight edge.)

Muff or cylinder glass: An elongated balloon of molten glass is blown. The round ends are cut off to form a cylinder shape like a muff which is then cut along its full length and relaxed in an annealing chamber until it becomes a flat rectangle.

Pot metal: Glass coloured throughout with one or more metallic oxides when molten in the pot.

Quarry: A square or diamond-shaped piece of glass, usually white. Plain, unpainted quarry glazing is generally made up of diamond shapes which serve to carry the combined weight of glass and lead vertically without the distortion frequently encountered in the horizontal stress pattern of square panes. (From the French *carré*, square.)

Tie bars: Panels within ferramenta or T-bars are held in a stable position by being tied at intervals to cross bars. The tie of lead or copper is soldered on to strong points in the intersections of cames and attached firmly to the bar. These are sometimes called 'saddle bars' and can be round or square sections. There is some advantage using a square section as there is less likelihood of the copper tie being torn loose from the solder when tightened.

Yellow stain: A stain ranging from pale lemon to orange, produced by applying a solution of silver compound – usually to the exterior surface of the glass, which, when fired, turns yellow. Sometimes called 'silver stain'.

SOURCES OF INFORMATION

Information on specialist conservation workshops can be obtained from

THE COUNCIL FOR THE CARE OF CHURCHES tel: 071-638 0971
    83 London Wall
    London EC2M 5NA

ENGLISH HERITAGE tel: 071-973 3000
    The Historic Buildings and Monuments Commission for England
    Contents Grants, Room 343 Fortress House
    23 Savile Row
    London W1X 2HE

In the absence of any national professional accreditation scheme, both bodies keep a detailed up-to-date list of approved conservators compiled on the basis of experience of the individual's work, range of experience and methods. This information is maintained and compiled independently from any pressure from either the trade or individuals.

The BRITISH CORPUS VITREARUM ARCHIVE at the NATIONAL MONUMENTS RECORD of the ROYAL COMMISSION ON HISTORICAL MONUMENTS FOR ENGLAND at Fortress House
    tel: 071-973 3500
    23 Savile Row
    London W1X 1AB
is open to the public from 10am to 5.30pm Monday-Friday.
The Archive aims to provide comprehensive coverage of the surviving medieval glass in Britain, and holds computerised records of photographic and related documentary material on glass of many periods from all contexts. Copies of the conservation records of glass conserved with grant aid from the HBMC and the CCC are held here, and the Archive welcomes material to augment the collection. The RCHM can advise on all aspects of photographing glass and is particularly concerned to be informed of requests to record threatened glass, damaged glass and glass at risk. Written requests for background on the dates and iconography of glass will be answered if accompanied by clearly legible photographs.

The GLASS INFORMATION CENTRE of the WORSHIPFUL COMPANY OF GLAZIERS AND PAINTERS OF GLASS
tel: 071-403 3300
Glaziers Hall
9 Montague Close
London Bridge
London SE1 9DD
acts as a clearing house and contact point for information on the trade and supply of glass in the UK, and contains the LONDON STAINED GLASS REPOSITORY which salvages and secures unwanted glass for re-use. They also provide information on all aspects of training and apprenticeship schemes for glaziers.

The BRITISH SOCIETY OF MASTER GLASS PAINTERS
6 Queen Square
London WC1
will respond to written requests for information on practising glaziers and all aspects of commissioning contemporary glass.

The BRITISH GLASS MANUFACTURERS CONFEDERATION
tel: 0742 686201
Northumberland Road
Sheffield
South Yorkshire
S10 2UA
provides a specialised library and information service on all aspects of glass manufacture.

FURTHER READING

STAINED GLASS BEFORE 1540, AN ANNOTATED BIBLIOGRAPHY by Madeline Harrison Caviness. (1983) published by G.K.Hall and Co, 70 Lincoln Street, Boston, Massachusetts.
An extremely useful and informative publication on medieval glass. It contains references to all aspects of glass conservation, techniques of glass painting, historical studies, topographical material, glass painters and designers, collections, sales and exhibition catalogues, and authors. The introduction is a particularly lucid and interesting account of the subject.

THE DETERIORATION AND CONSERVATION OF PAINTED GLASS: A CRITICAL BIBLIOGRAPHY by R. G. Newton. (1982) published for the British Academy by the Oxford University Press as Corpus Vitrearum Medii Aevi Great Britain Occasional Papers II.
A highly individual and informative book which covers Professor Newton's views on the state of the art and science of glass conservation up to 1982.

STAINED GLASS by L. Lee, G. Seddon and F. Stephens. (1976) published by Mitchell Beazley.
The best general book on glass as an artist's medium. Includes a brief history of glass, and an account of its manufacture and conservation. This book has very informative and well-chosen illustrations and provides an excellent overview of the art and craft.

TWO THOUSAND YEARS OF FLAT GLASS MAKING by I. Burgoyne and R. Scobie. (1983) published by Pilkington Brothers plc.
An inexpensive and well-illustrated account of the development and manufacture of window glass from Roman times to the present day.

VICTORIAN STAINED GLASS by M. Harrison. (1980) published by Barrie and Jenkins.
The first comprehensive survey of nineteenth-century stained glass, this highly readable and superbly illustrated book is an essential guide to the styles, development and identification of nineteenth-century stained glass artists and workshops.

PRACTICAL BUILDING CONSERVATION (ENGLISH HERITAGE TECHNICAL HANDBOOK) John Ashurst et al. (1988) published by Gower Technical Press. Vol. 1: Stone Masonry, Vol. 2: Brick and Terracotta and Earth, Vol. 3: Mortars, Plasters and Renders, Vol. 4: Metals, Vol. 5: Wood, Glass and Resins and Technical Bibliography.
These five volumes contain the collective experience and knowledge of the Historic Buildings and Monuments Commission for England

(English Heritage), formerly the Directorate of Ancient Monuments and Historic Buildings of the Department of the Environment and the Office of Public Buildings and Works. The Research, Technical and Advisory Services Group have collated their collective expertise in the theory and practice of conserving buildings and the historic materials used in their construction. These volumes are directed towards answering the principal problems and requests for information.

A GUIDE TO CHURCH INSPECTION AND REPAIR (1986) published by Church House Publishing.
An introduction to the quinquennial inspection system for churches, and procedures for repair works.